# Wee Co



# Wee Sing®

# King Cole's Party

## A Coloring Activity Book of Songs From the Video

Wee Sing books by Pamela Conn Beall and Susan Hagen Nipp
Illustrated by Kelly McMahon


Published by Price Stern Sloan, Inc.
360 North La Cienega Boulevard, Los Angeles, California 90048

ISBN: 0-8431-4728-8

10 9 8 7 6 5 4 3 2 1



PRICE STERN SLOAN
Los Angeles

Draw a castle.

castle

Trace the word.

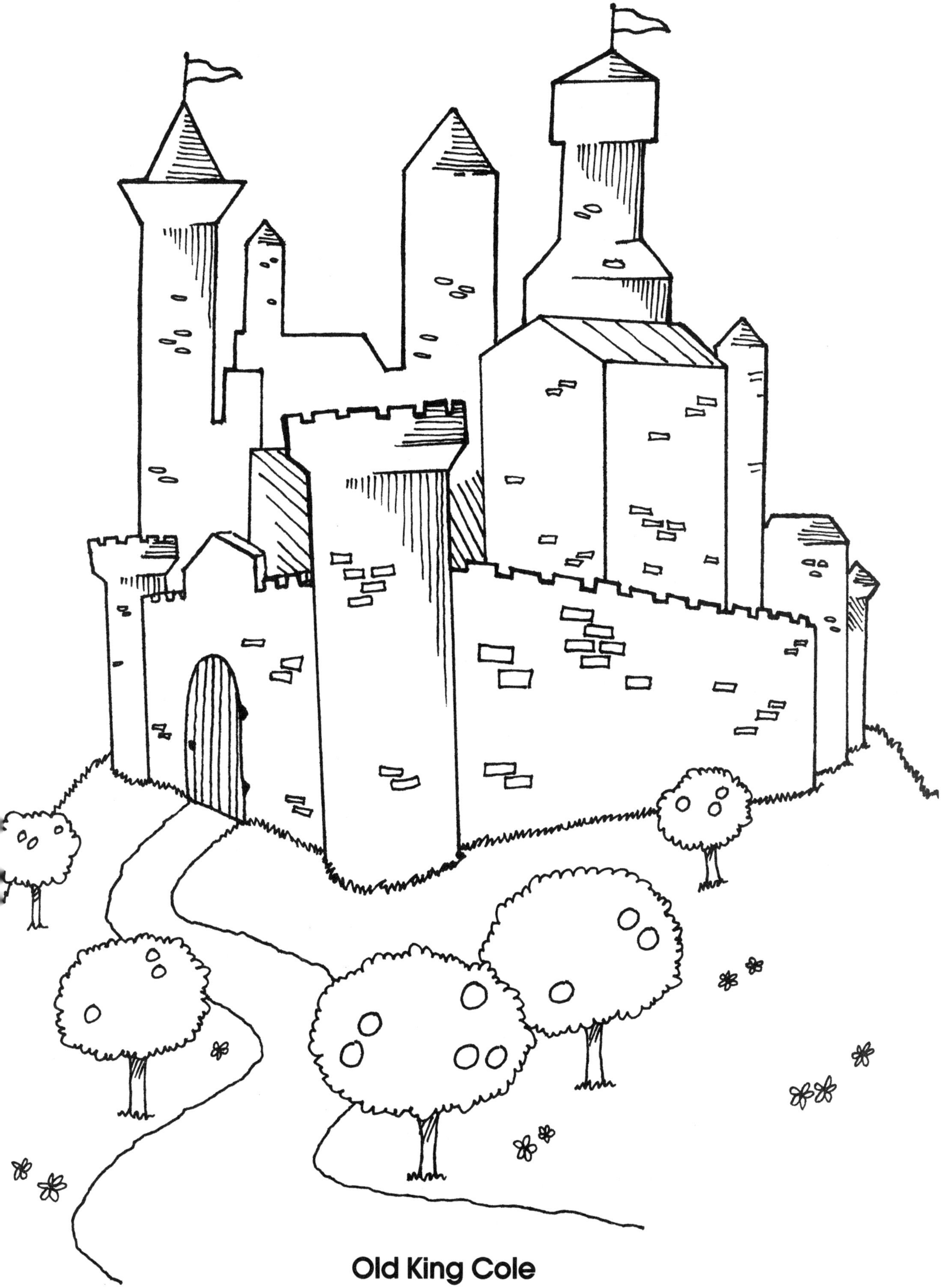

Old King Cole

Circle the things you eat with butter.

Betty Botter

Decorate the cake.

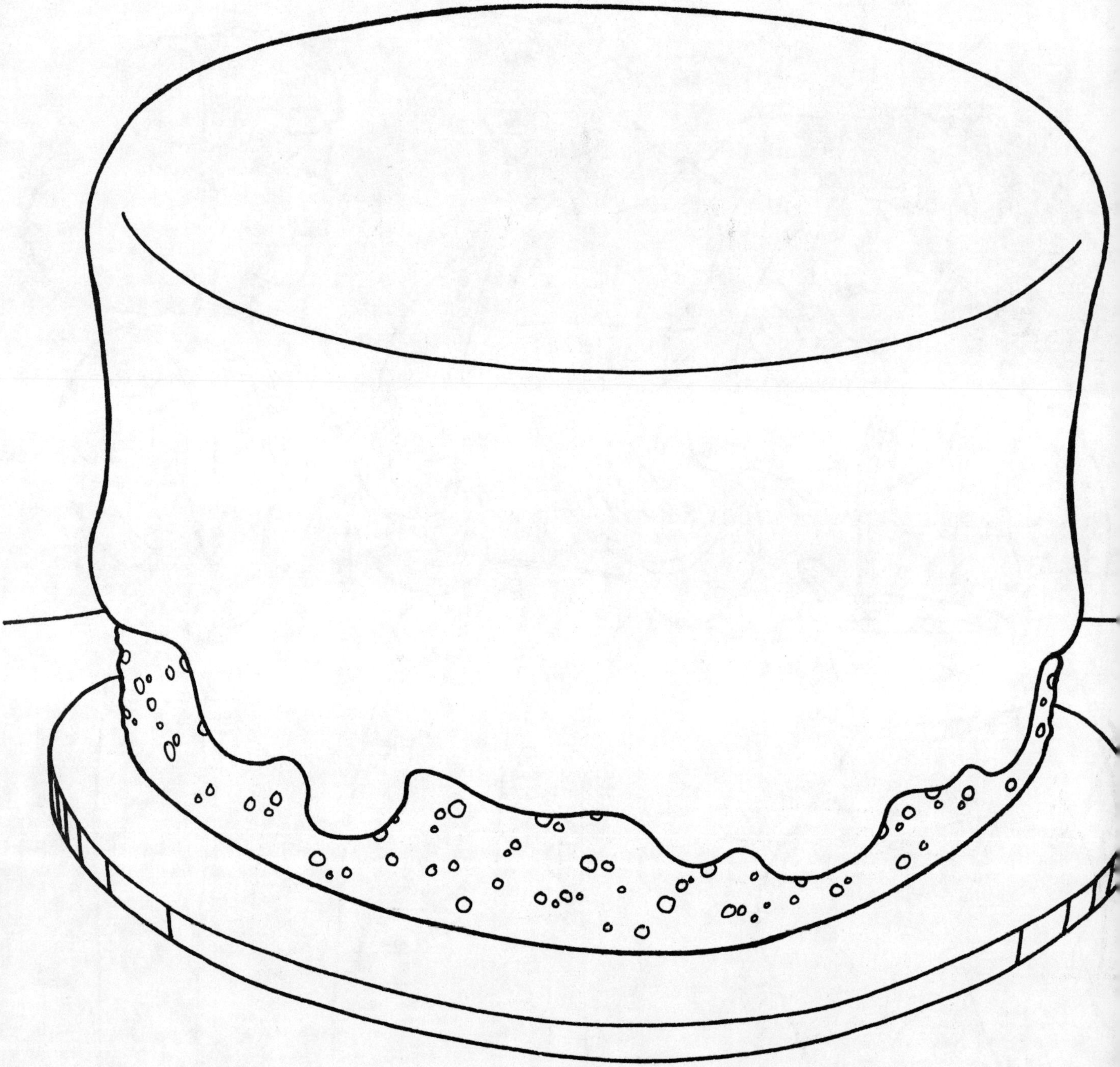

Pat-A-Cake

Draw the missing parts of the kettles.

Polly Put The Kettle On

Count the blackbirds.

22 23 24

Trace the number.

Sing A Song Of Sixpence

Draw a circle around the hot things. Draw a square around the cold things.

Pease Porridge Hot

Circle the matching pails.

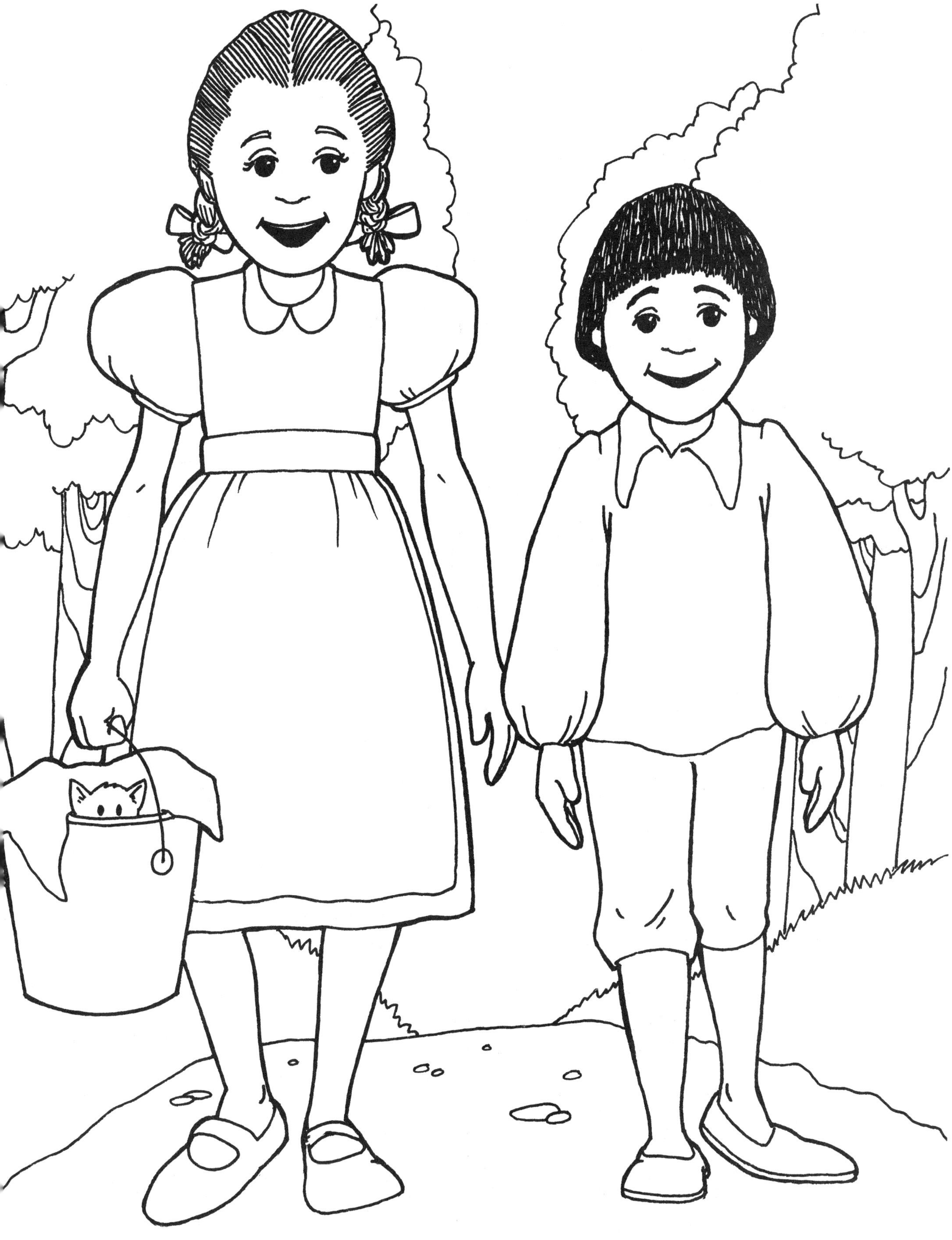

Jack And Jill

Color the things Mary could make from her lamb's wool.

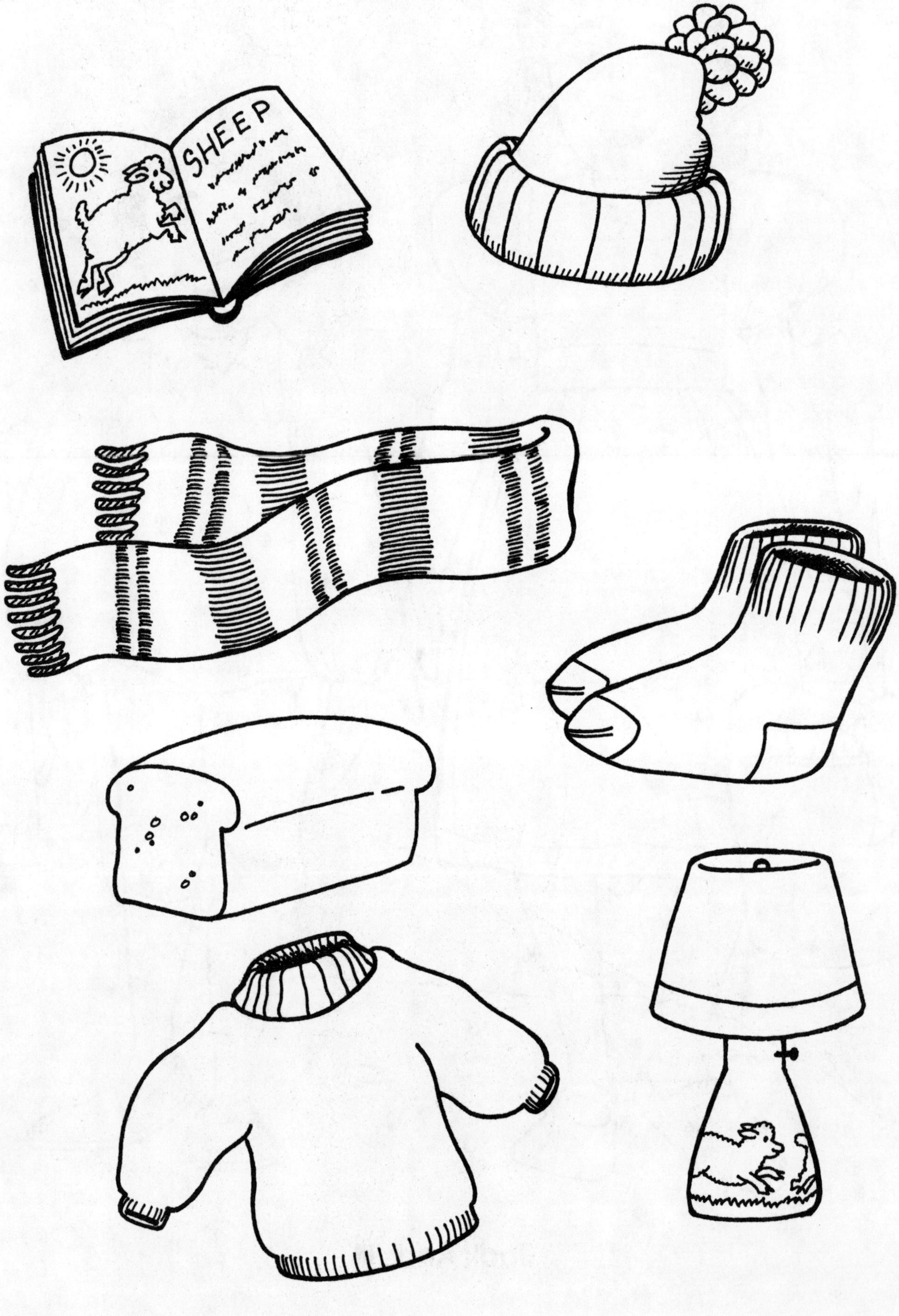

Mary Had A Little Lamb

Count the cows. Count the sheep. How many in all?

Little Boy Blue

Color the presents. Write the number.

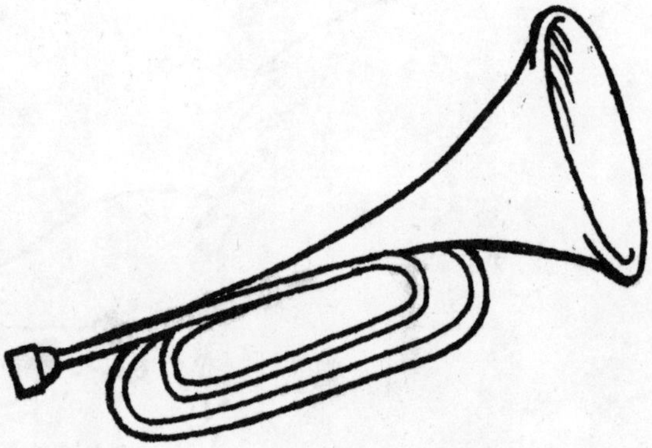

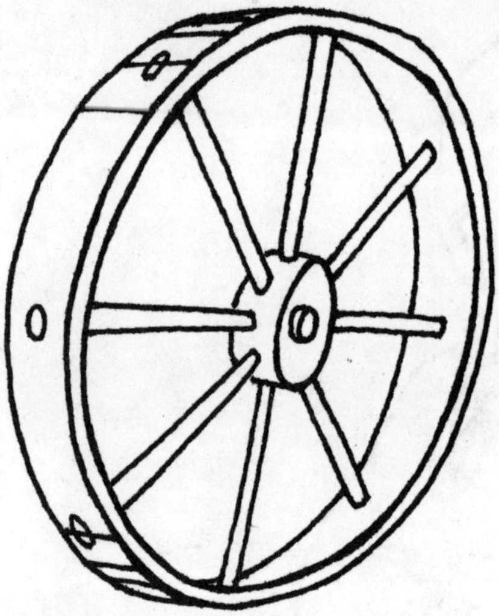

Walking Chant

Draw a line from the ducks to the places they can swim.

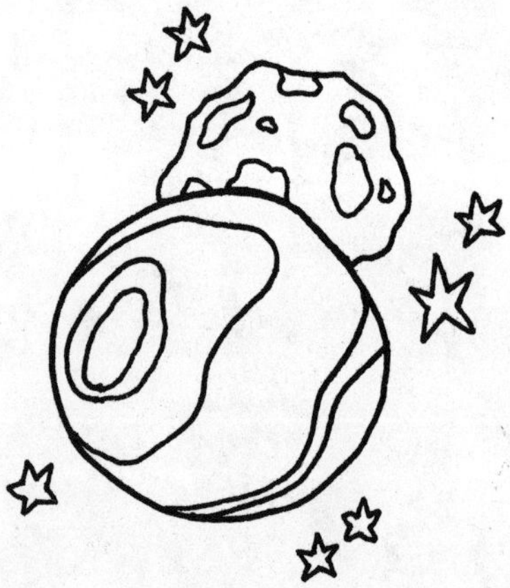

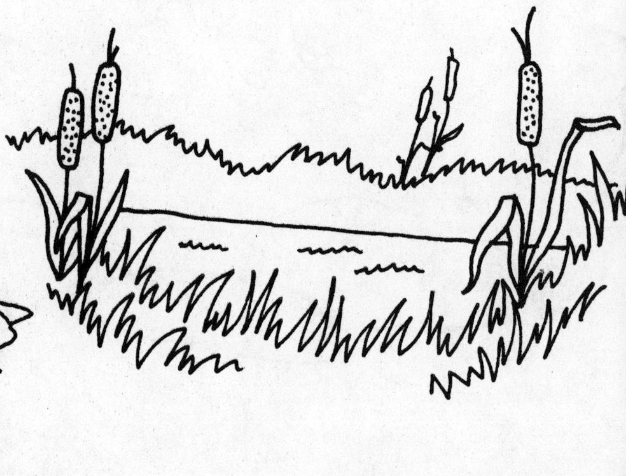

Six Little Ducks

Help the children get to London.

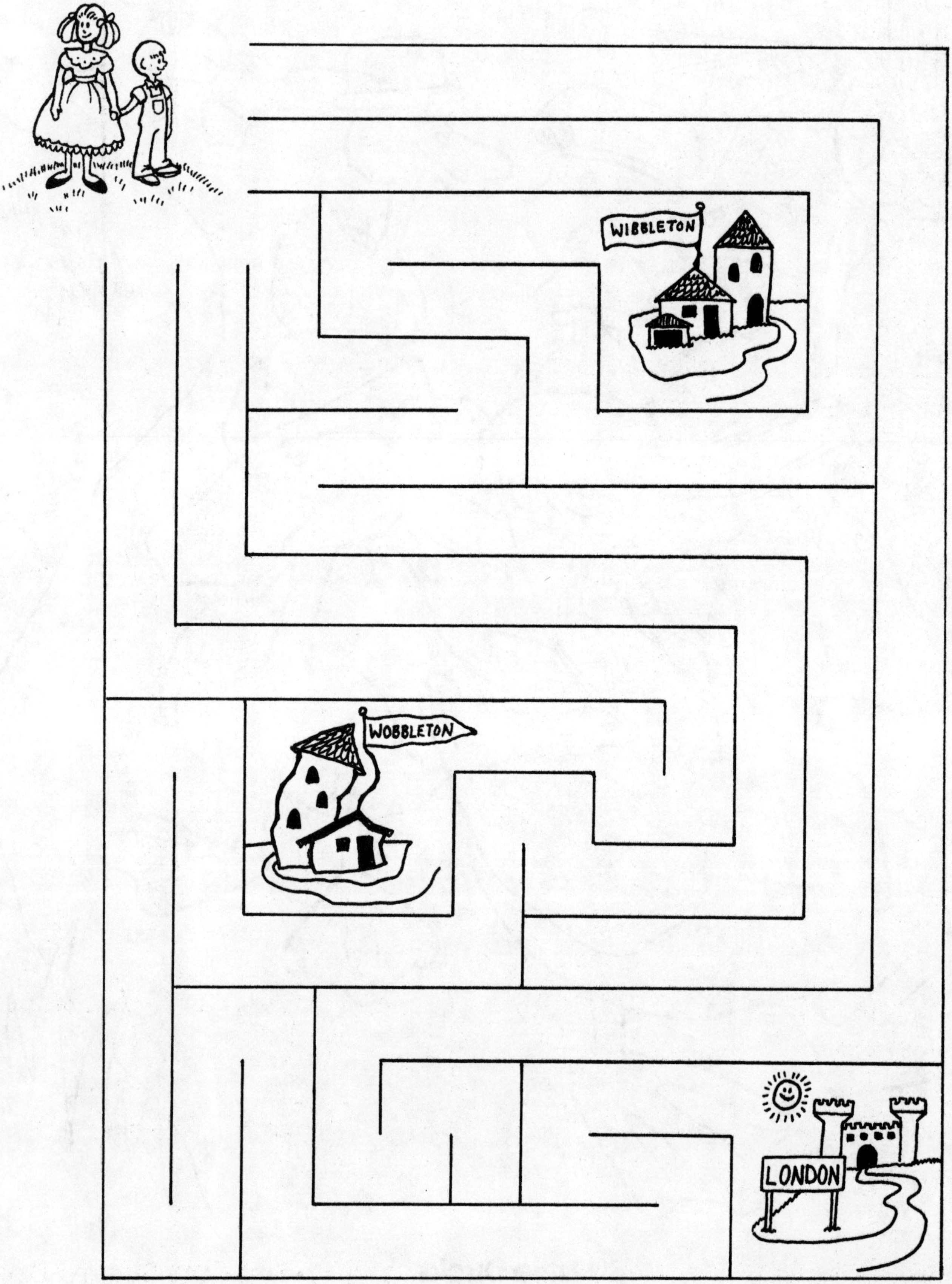

ere Was A Crooked Man • Wibbleton To Wobbleton • See-Saw Sac-Ra-Down

Can you find these words in the word search? Read across and down. Circle each word as you find it.

Bill

| | | | |
|---|---|---|---|
| THIS | SEVEN | DOG | HIVE |
| OLD | EIGHT | BONE | STICKS |
| MAN | NINE | HOME | GATE |
| FIVE | THUMB | SHOE | SPINE |

| | | | | | | | | |
|---|---|---|---|---|---|---|---|---|
| S | A | T | H | I | S | F | R | E |
| T | S | H | O | E | P | I | C | M |
| I | G | U | M | H | I | V | E | B |
| C | A | M | A | N | N | E | P | R |
| K | T | B | O | N | E | L | R | E |
| S | E | V | E | N | O | Q | U | I |
| U | B | R | W | I | F | D | O | G |
| D | I | O | Y | N | I | M | L | H |
| T | H | O | M | E | D | O | D | T |

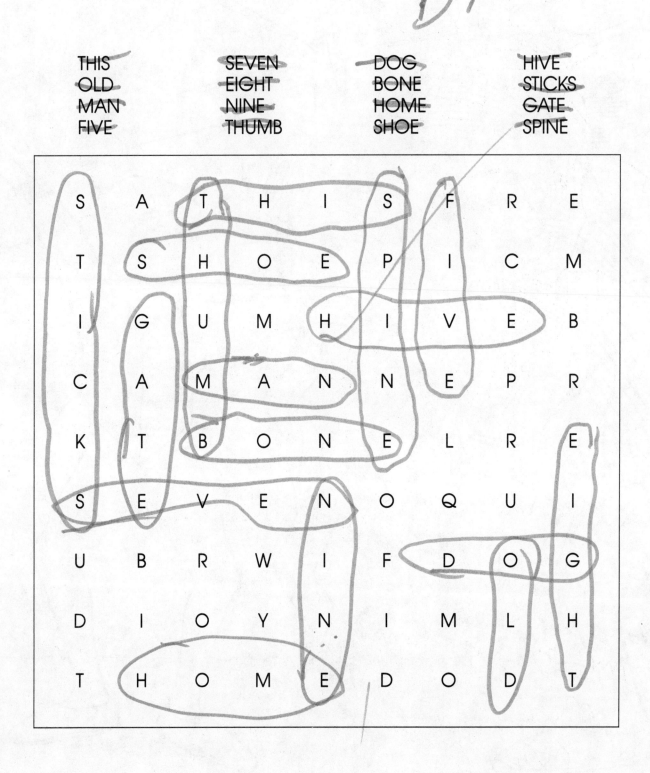

This Old Man

Connect the dots.

Humpty Dumpty

Help Bo Peep find her seven sheep.

Little Bo-Peep

How many plums are in the tree? Write the number.

Little Jack Horner

Draw a line from Jack Sprat to the food he would eat and from Mrs. Sprat to the food she would eat.

By Brittany

Jack Sprat

Help the spider get to the curds.

By Brittany

by Brittany

Little Miss Muffet

bY Andrea

Color the things you use in the tub.

Rub-A-Dub-Dub

Draw a line from each number to the correct picture.

1

2

3

4

5

Jack Be Nimble

Draw your favorite food.

food

Trace the word.

Little Tommy Tucker

Can you find eight P's?

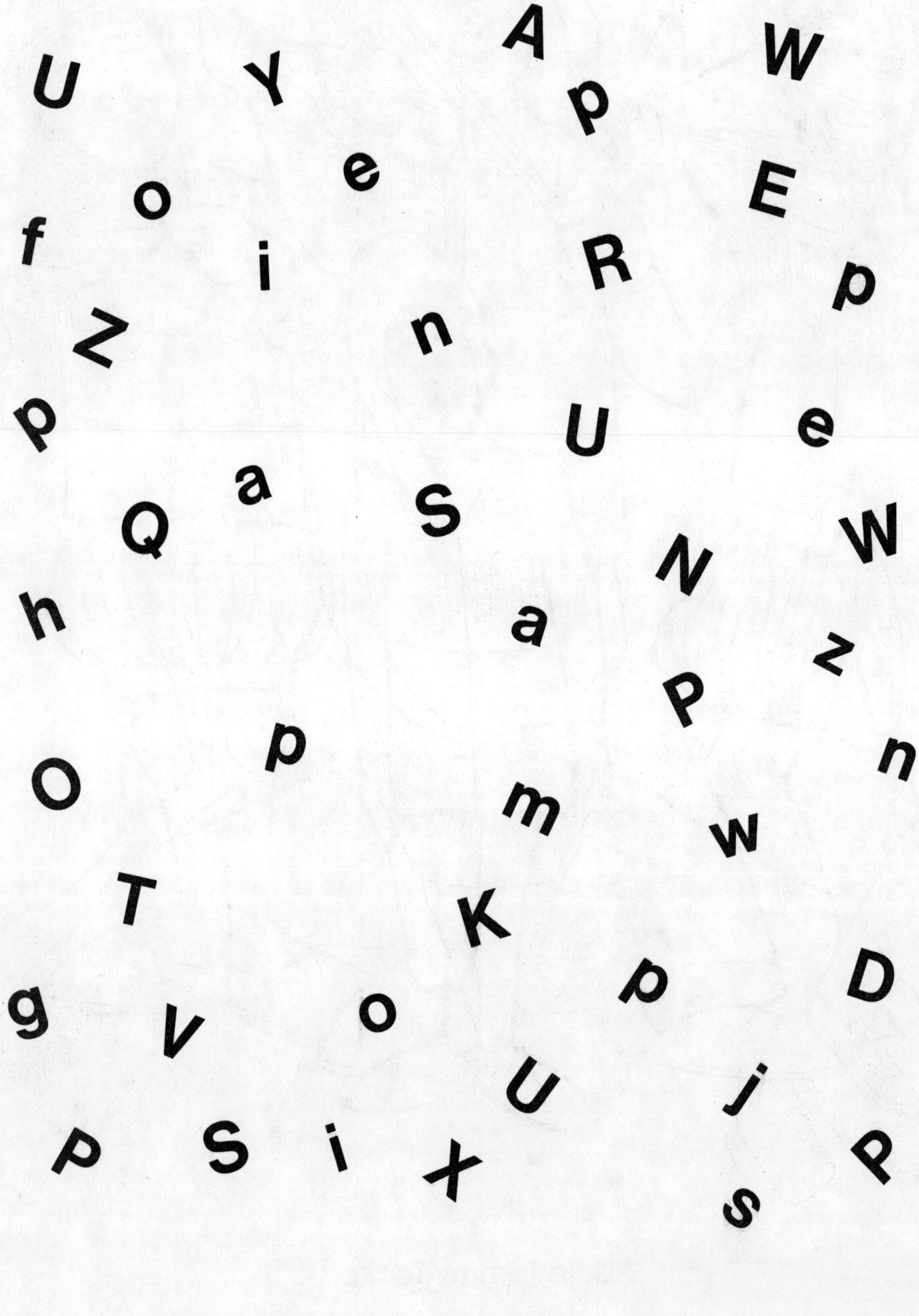

Peter Piper

Draw crowns on the King and Queen.

Old King Cole

# Wee Color®

WEE COLOR® books feature favorite songs collected from the best-selling Wee Sing® books, plus fun-filled activities.

WEE COLOR WEE SING

WEE COLOR WEE SING AND PLAY

WEE COLOR WEE SING SILLY SONGS

WEE COLOR WEE SING AROUND THE CAMPFIRE

WEE COLOR WEE SING FOR CHRISTMAS

WEE COLOR WEE SING NURSERY RHYMES AND LULLABIES

WEE COLOR WEE SING BIBLE SONGS

WEE COLOR WEE SING AMERICA

WEE COLOR WEE SING AUSTRALIA

WEE COLOR WEE SING KING COLE'S PARTY

WEE COLOR WEE SING TOGETHER

WEE COLOR WEE SING DINOSAURS

(Each Wee Color Wee Sing activity package contains a book, 6 felt-tipped markers and a 30-minute cassette.)

The Wee Color Wee Sing series is available wherever books are sold or may be ordered directly from the publisher.

PRICE STERN SLOAN
360 North La Cienega Boulevard, Los Angeles, CA 90048-1925